# SAINT FRANCIS
# and the ANIMALS

*by Leo Politi*

Charles Scribner's Sons

NEW YORK

# FRANCIS OF ASSISI

Long ago in Italy, a young man named Francis Bernardone lived near the town of Assisi.

Francis loved the countryside. He loved the rich earth, the running streams, the blue sky, the bright sun, the trees and the flowers, and all the other things of God's creation.

Once he had been a rich young man but he had left his home and his riches. His one wish was to live simply and help others.

Men who wished to do the same came to live and work with him. Francis called them his brothers.

Francis loved people and he loved birds and animals. He would even pick up the worms from his path and put them in a safe place so they would not be stepped on by people passing by.

He always helped and protected animals and because he wanted to feel close to them he called them

*miei fratelli e sorelle*

my brothers and sisters.

# FRANCIS PREACHES TO THE BIRDS

One day as Francis was walking through the countryside with two of the brothers, he saw on the trees and on the ground a great number of birds.

Wondering at the sight, he said to his companion:

"Let us stay here for a while. I wish to preach to my sisters, the birds."

And going into the fields he began to preach to the birds. As he walked among them and touched them with his robe, not even one flew away. The birds on the trees flew down to listen to him.

Francis said to them:

"O birds, my little sisters, praise God your Creator for he has given you freedom to fly wherever you like. He feeds you, and has given you the streams to drink from, the hills to shelter you, and the trees where you can build your nests. God also clothes you and your children with feathers. Therefore my little sisters, praise God who loves you dearly and has given you so many blessings."

After Francis finished speaking, all the birds began to sing and to spread their wings. With reverence they bowed their heads to the ground. By their acts and their song they showed that Francis had given them great joy.

Finally, when he blessed them, all the birds rose up together in the air with marvelous songs.

# THE LITTLE HARE

One day, a little hare was caught in a trap and one of the brothers set it free and carried it, still alive, to Francis.

When Francis saw it, he felt sorry for the gentle creature and said:

"Little Brother Hare, come to me. Why did you let yourself be trapped?"

When the brother who had been carrying the hare let it go, it ran straight to Francis' lap, as if to show it felt safe with him. After it rested there for a while, Francis set the little hare down on the ground that it might be free to return to its home in the fields.

Yet, as often as he set it down, the little hare climbed back on Francis' lap.

# THE BOY WITH THE DOVES

One day Francis met a boy with a cage of doves which he had caught and brought to sell at the market place. The brother felt very sorry for the doves and said to the boy:

"Oh good youth, I wish you would give them to me so that these humble and innocent birds may not fall into the hands of some cruel person."

The boy, who was very devoted to Francis, knowing how the brother loved birds so well, gladly gave them to him. As children came and grouped around to see, Francis took one of the doves in his hands and as he held it he said to the children:

"Are not doves sweet and gentle?"

Then he said to the doves:

"*Mie care sorelle,* my dear sisters, do no longer fear, for I will take you home and protect you, and will make nests for you, so that you may increase and multiply, according to the commandment of God your Creator."

And when he took them home, Francis made nests for them on the trees near his cave. And the doves laid eggs in the nests and hatched them. Without fear they lived happily with their families among the brothers, by whom they were fed.

And all day long they fluttered around and filled the air with sweet sounds.

## THE PHEASANT THAT REFUSED
## TO EAT

One time when Francis was ill, a nobleman sent him a beautiful pheasant. The brother was very pleased with the gift. He held it close to him and spoke to it with loving words. Then he said to his companions:

"Now we will see if Brother Pheasant prefers to stay with us, or wants to be free and fly back to the woods."

He asked one of the brothers if he would carry the pheasant some distance away. This the brother did. But no sooner was the bird set free than it flew back to Francis. The pheasant was carried still farther away, but returned again and again.

As they tried for the last time, the brothers jokingly blocked the entrance to the cave to see if the bird would still try to reach Francis. The pheasant made its way again by slipping between the robes of the brothers.

One day a doctor who was a friend of Francis saw the pheasant and asked if he might have the bird, because he wanted to take care of it.

But when he carried the pheasant home, the bird, as though protesting against parting from Francis, refused to eat. Amazed, the doctor carried the bird back to the brother, and told him what had happened.

When the pheasant saw Francis it was happy and began to eat again.

## FRANCIS AND THE FISH

Once when Francis was sitting in a boat near the shore of a lake, a fisherman caught a large fish. As a token of friendship, the fisherman brought it to the brother. Francis accepted the fish joyfully and thanked the man. Then when the fisherman had gone, he said to the fish:

"Brother fish, why did you allow yourself to be caught?" As he put the fish back into the water he said to it:

"From now on be careful and don't let anyone catch you again!"

As though it wanted to show his gratitude to Francis, the fish played happily beside the boat, and did not swim away from the spot until later, when Francis blessed it and bade it farewell.

# FRANCIS AND THE LAMB

One day as Francis was journeying through the countryside
he saw in the fields a shepherd watching over a flock of goats and

sheep. Among these was a single lamb which meekly ran beside the flock, grazing quietly by itself. It seemed very sad. When Francis saw this he felt sorry and approached the lonely and gentle creature.

"Come to me, little lamb," he said.

The lamb liked Francis because immediately it came close and, bleating, put its front feet up on the brother's robe. Francis spoke gently to the lamb and said:

"I will buy you and take you away from the company of all these goats."

But having nothing except his poor garments, Francis offered the shepherd his cloak in trade for the lamb.

The man agreed to trade.

Now the lamb was happy and followed Francis everywhere he went. At night it lay on the ground close to Francis and fell asleep.

# THE WOLF OF GUBBIO

At another time the people of the town of Gubbio were un-happy because of a ferocious wolf who not only devoured animals, but even people, and prowled around giving no one any peace by day or night.

Children were afraid and dogs barked.

The men went armed with guns to work in the fields, and the mothers were afraid to let the children go out to play. Even the dogs were frightened and barked at the wolf.

Feeling sorry for the people, and mostly for the helpless children and little animals who had to live in constant fear, Francis decided to do something about it.

He knew the wolf alone was not to be blamed, but the people as well, for they had never spoken to him with kind words, and had never tried to make a friend of him. After all, he too was one of God's creatures, and only destroyed because of hunger—not for amusement.

Against the advice of the people Francis went out of the town gate to meet the wolf. Some of the brothers went with him. They and the people waited at a safe distance to see what would happen.

The air was filled with suspense as Francis came near the wolf. Then suddenly the silence was broken by a loud growl from the ferocious animal who rushed at Francis with his mouth wide open, showing his big, sharp teeth.

Calmly, Francis made the sign of the cross over him, and said gently:

"I command you, Brother Wolf, in the name of God, not to harm me or anyone else."

Because of the gentle voice, the wolf knew he was being spoken to with kindness, something that had never happened to him before. Meek as a lamb he lay down at Francis' feet.

Then Francis spoke to him again:

"Brother Wolf, you have done much evil in this land, destroying and killing. For this all the people of Gubbio hate you. But I, Brother Wolf, wish to make peace between you and them. If you will offend no more, they will pardon you and neither man nor dog will harm you."

As though he had understood every word, the wolf showed by the movement of his tail and his ears, and by bowing his head, that he agreed with Francis and was willing to accept his decision.

Then Francis said:

"Since you are willing to make this peace I promise that as long as you live the people of this town will give you the food you need. You shall never go hungry again, for I know hunger made you do this evil."

And when Francis stretched out his hand, the wolf lifted up his paw and placed it in the brother's hand, as if making a promise to him.

And Francis, speaking to the wolf again, said:

"Brother Wolf, I command you in the name of God to follow me." The wolf obeyed and walked by his side through the town, among the people, who stood by and watched with great amazement.

The news spread to every corner of town.

"Brother Francis caught the wolf!" children called, and all the people, great and small, old and young, hurried to the public square to see Francis and the wolf.

When all the people had come together Francis spoke to them:

"Listen, my brothers. Brother Wolf, who is here before you, has promised to make peace with you, and will never again harm people or animals, if you promise to give him the food he needs each day. If you consent I promise he will keep his agreement."

Then all the people with one voice promised to feed the wolf.

As if to show that he was willing, the wolf knelt down, bowed his head, and lifted up his paw and placed it in the hands of Francis.

From that day on, the wolf went tamely from door to door, and even into the houses. All the people received him courteously and fed him with great pleasure. The children played with him, as though he were a big dog and no dog barked at him as he went about. So the town of Gubbio lived in peace and happiness.

In later years the Church said that Francis, because of his pure and holy life, should be called Saint Francis.

And that is what we call him today:

SAINT FRANCIS OF ASSISI